NON-VERBAL REASONING FOR 11+

2D TESTS WORKBOOK 1

Fully classroom-tested by Teachitright pupils and approved by parents

- Odd ones out

- Matrices

- Analogies

- Sequences

Copyright information

Billy the Bookworm™ is the property of Teachitright

Author

Chris Pearse

The author has asserted his moral right under the Copyright, Designs and Patents Act, 1988, to be identified as the author of this work.

First published in Great Britain in 2018 by

The University of Buckingham Press
Yeomanry House
Hunter Street
Buckingham MK18 1EG

A CIP catalogue record for this book is available at the British Library

ISBN 9781908684714

Teachitright

Teachitright is one of the most successful 11+ tuition companies in the South-East. In the last 10 years we've supported thousands of pupils for both grammar school and independent school entry. We have tuition centres across Buckinghamshire, Berkshire and Surrey.

Based on our wealth of experience and knowledge, we have produced a range of books that will help support your child through their 11+ journey in both CEM style and traditional 11+ tests and many Common Entrance exams. Our books, written by qualified teachers, have been classroom tested with pupils and adapted to ensure children are fully prepared and able to perform to the best of their ability.

Our unique mascot, Billy the Bookworm, will help guide children through the book and gives helpful hints and tips throughout.

We hope you find this book very useful and informative and wish you luck on your 11+ journey.

Teachitright holds a number of comprehensive revision courses and mock exams throughout the year. If you would like to find out more information, please visit:

www.teachitright.com

Introduction

This Non-Verbal Reasoning 2D Workbook 1 provides the perfect preparation for both 11+ and Common Entrance exams. This book contains the key topics: Odd one out, Sequences, Matrices and Analogies

How to use this book

As this book is broken down into lessons that cover different topics, it can be used to focus on individual areas of development or to work through every topic.

Learn: An informative teaching section to help with the key points and techniques for that lesson topic. It includes worked examples.

Develop: Opportunity to practise non-verbal reasoning question types and to ensure key principles and techniques are fully understood.

Timed tests: Strategically placed progressive timed tests to help build confidence with non-verbal reasoning questions and time management.

The answer section gives detailed explanations to aid revision. There is also a glossary on page 65. It is important for the pupils to understand the correct non-verbal reasoning vocabulary to help aid their knowledge.

In the back of the book is a marking chart and progress grid to help track your child's development throughout the topics and to highlight strengths and weaknesses.

Contents

LESSON 1:
ODD ONE OUT

Look out for Billy's tips and hints.

LEARN

This question type involves spotting the odd one out. It is often easier to group four figures together that have something in common, as this then leaves the one figure that's different from all the others.

Warm-up task

To help improve your observation skills choose five everyday items and try to identify the odd one out. Below are three examples to get you started and to help you think about how things can be grouped together to leave one odd one out. Look at sizes, shapes, colours and anything else that might make one item different from another.

1.

The 2p coin could be the odd one out because of the shading.

2.

The rugby ball could be the odd one out because it is not round.

3.

The pencil could be the odd one out because it has an eraser on its end.

For the more challenging questions you will need to consider more than one feature. The answer might be to do with how the features of a figure are linked together. For example, you might need to count the number of sides or corners of shapes. In the example below there are twice as many sides on the outer shape as there are small triangles inside. However, if you add up the sides on the 3 triangles, you have 9 sides.

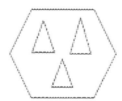

Linking features (sometimes called elements or properties) in figures is something you will need to do in the timed section later in this chapter. Remember to think about how the features work together.

Worked example

Find the figure that is the odd one out in these five figures.

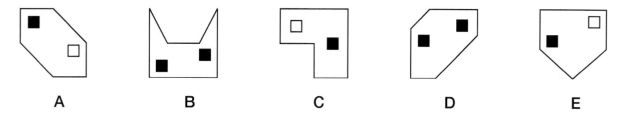

| A | B | C | D | E |

Method

(1)   Firstly, look at each figure and its features. Work from left to right to ensure you don't miss any options.

2)   Identify whether any of the figures have any common features. For example, here you might notice that they all have small squares inside the larger outer shape. However, some are pairs of white and black squares and some are pairs of black squares, so you can't use this to find the odd one out.

(3)   Look at another part of the figures. The outer shapes all look different and often it is worth counting how many sides the shapes have. To avoid counting the same side again, it is helpful to place a line on each edge as shown below, and then to write the number of sides above each shape to identify if there are any patterns.

(4)   If you count the sides on each outer shape, you will find that E has 5 sides while the rest of the shapes all have 6 sides. So, E is the odd one out.

Remember if you have checked all the variables (features that vary), do consider rotation. It can help to turn your page, so you can look at all the figures the same way up.

DEVELOP

Here are some to try for yourself.

1.

   A   B   C   D   E

2.

   A   B   C   D   E

3.

   A   B   C   D   E

4.

   A   B   C   D   E

TIMED TEST 1   *6 MINS*

Circle the letter for each correct answer.

1.

        A   B   C   D   E

2.

        A   B   C   D   E

3.

        A   B   C   D   E

4.

        A   B   C   D   E

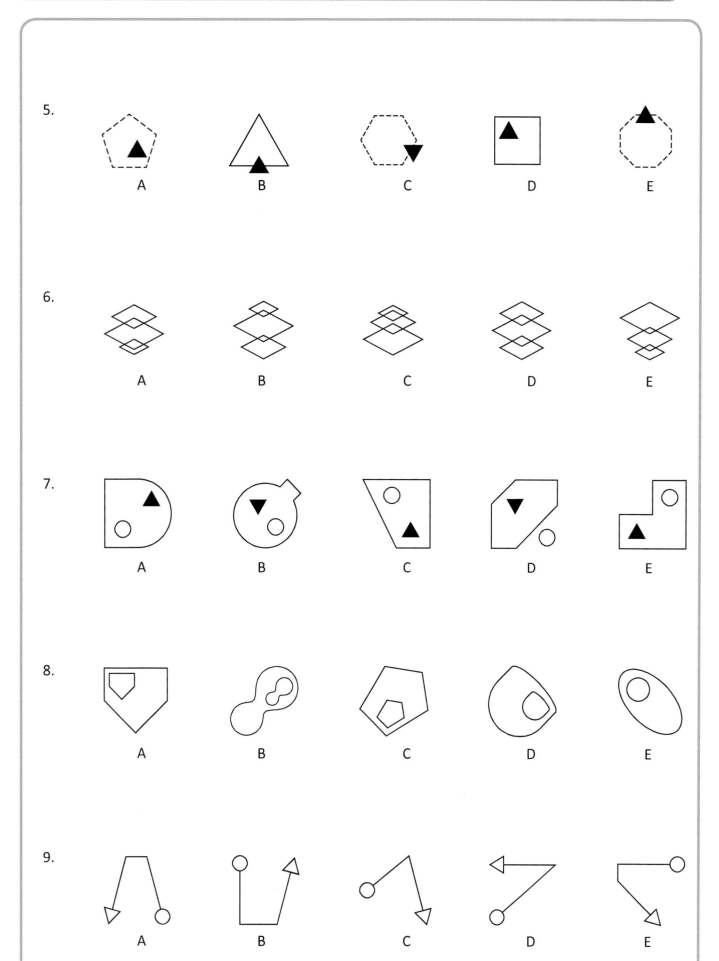

5.

   A   B   C   D   E

6.

   A   B   C   D   E

7.

   A   B   C   D   E

8.

   A   B   C   D   E

9.

   A   B   C   D   E

10.

   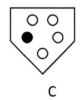   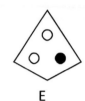

   A   B   C   D   E

11.

   A   B   C   D   E

12.

   A   B   C   D   E

TIMED TEST 2 **6 MINS**

Circle the letter for each correct answer.

1.

      A   B   C   D   E

2.

      A   B   C   D   E

3.

      A   B   C   D   E

4.

      A   B   C   D   E

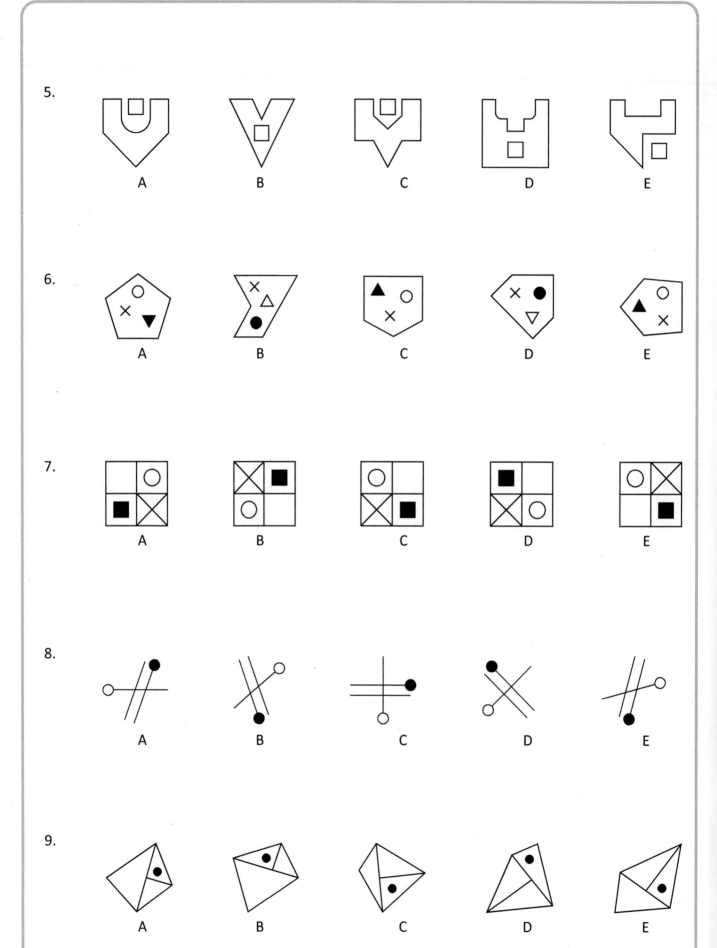

5.

A   B   C   D   E

6.

A   B   C   D   E

7.

A   B   C   D   E

8.

A   B   C   D   E

9.

A   B   C   D   E

10.

    A   B   C   D   E

11.

    A   B   C   D   E

12.

    A   B   C   D   E

TIMED TEST 3   6 MINS

Circle the letter for each correct answer.

1.

       A   B   C   D   E

2.

       A   B   C   D   E

3.

       A   B   C   D   E

4.

       A   B   C   D   E

5.

A   B   C   D   E

6.

A   B   C   D   E

7.

A   B   C   D   E

8.

A   B   C   D   E

9.

A   B   C   D   E

10.

   A   B   C   D   E

11.

   A   B   C   D   E

12.

   A   B   C   D   E

LESSON 2:
MATRICES

Look out for Billy's tips and hints.

LEARN

This question type involves finding the figure that completes the pattern in a grid in the best possible way. The patterns can be created along the rows or in columns or diagonally (in either direction). One very useful tip, is to draw what you think belongs in the empty box before looking at the answer options. This helps you imagine what the answer will look like.

Warm-up task

Try to draw the missing figure that fits in the empty box in the grid. Consider how the pattern has been created.

<table>
<tr><td align="center">1</td><td align="center">2</td><td align="center">3</td></tr>
<tr><td>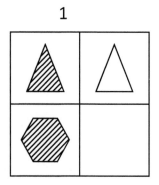</td><td>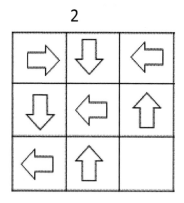</td><td>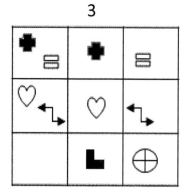</td></tr>
</table>

(1)   In grid 1 the connection works across the row and it is easy to identify the shape is the same. The shading changes from hatched to a blank shape. Therefore, it should be a blank hexagon.

(2)   It is sometimes worth looking at the whole grid to see if it makes a pattern. In grid 2 it has a series of arrows and it can be useful to check how they change from one box to the next. In this example the arrows in each row and column rotate 90° clockwise.

(3)   The final matrix is a common type where two columns are combined – in this case the left-hand column has been created by combining the other two columns.

Worked example

Choose the figure that best fills the empty box in the grid.

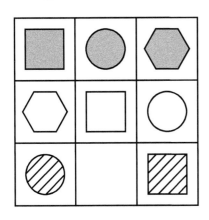

A   B   C

 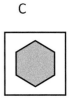

D   E   F

Method

(1)   First look at the whole grid to see if you can spot a pattern. If no immediate pattern can be seen, look at the rows first. All the shading must be the same in every row, so eliminate answer options A, C and E.

(2)   Going across the rows, think about a different feature. It is easy to spot that each row contains a square, a circle and a hexagon. Think about which shape is missing from the bottom row – a hexagon is clearly needed. B, D and F are all hexagons. However, hexagon F is positioned incorrectly, so eliminate F.

(3)   This leaves hexagons B and D. The only difference is the slant of the striped shading. The lines should be sloping from bottom left to top right. Therefore the option that completes the grid correctly is B.

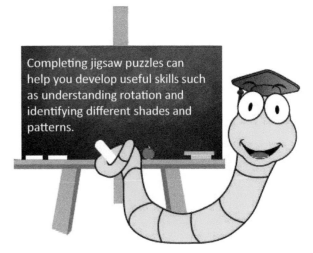

Completing jigsaw puzzles can help you develop useful skills such as understanding rotation and identifying different shades and patterns.

DEVELOP

Here are some to try for yourself.

1.

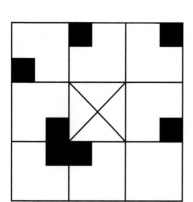

A   B   C

D   E   F

2.

A   B   C

D   E   F

3.

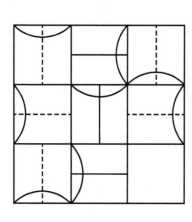

A   B   C

D   E   F

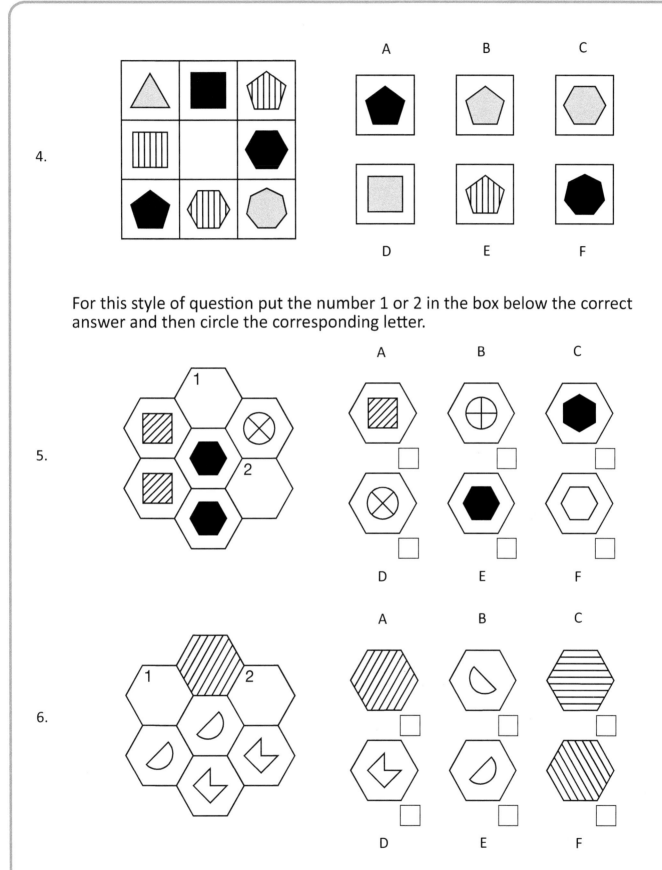

For this style of question put the number 1 or 2 in the box below the correct answer and then circle the corresponding letter.

TIMED TEST 1   5 MINS

Circle the letter for each correct answer.

1.

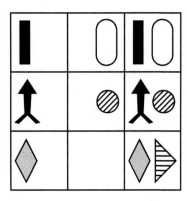

A   B   C

D   E   F

2.

A   B   C

D   E   F

3.

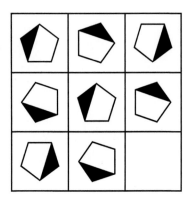

A   B   C

D   E   F

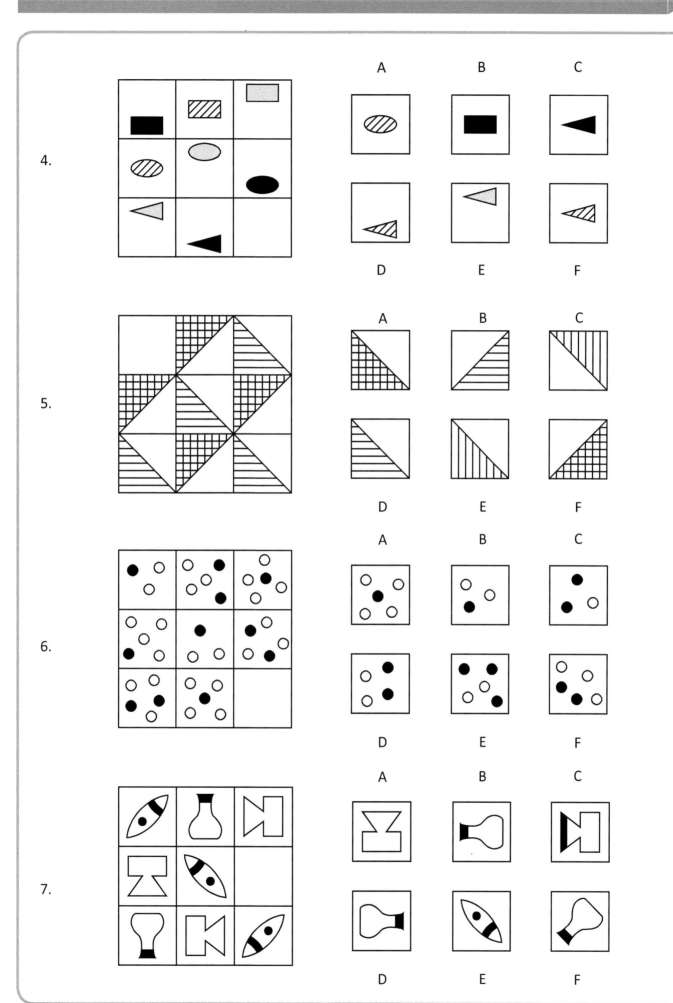

8.

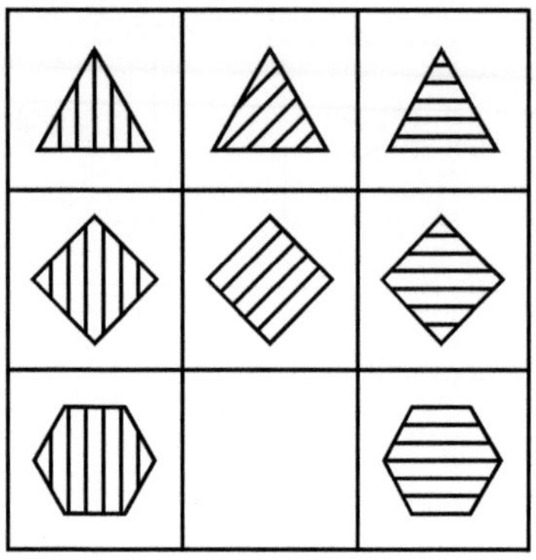

A   B   C

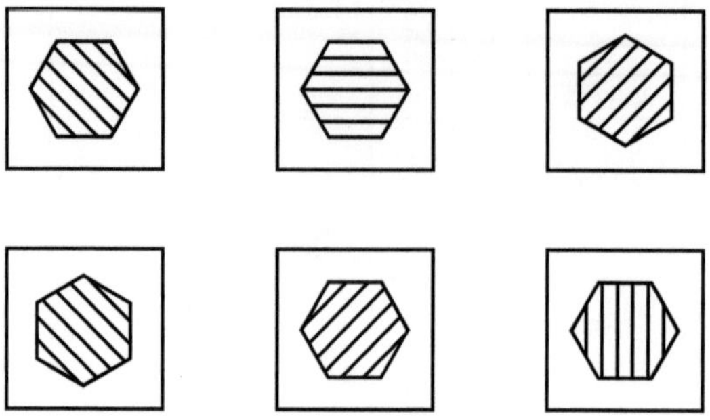

D   E   F

9.

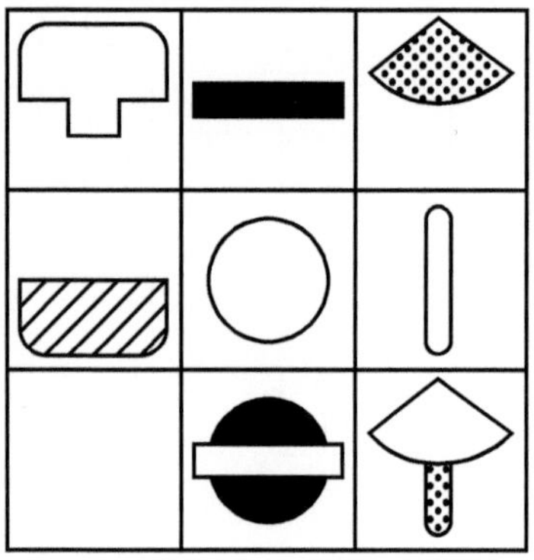

A   B   C

D   E   F

10.

A   B   C

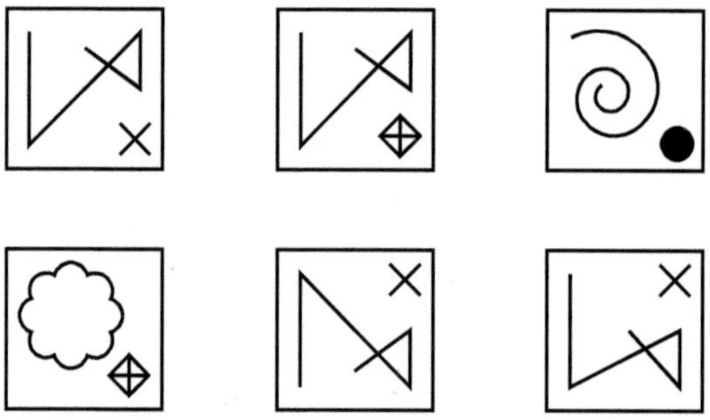

D   E   F

TIMED TEST 2   **5 MINS**

Circle the letter for each correct answer.

1.

   A   B   C

   D   E   F

2.

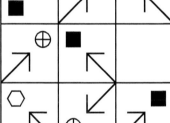

   A   B   C

   D   E   F

3.

   A   B   C

   D   E   F

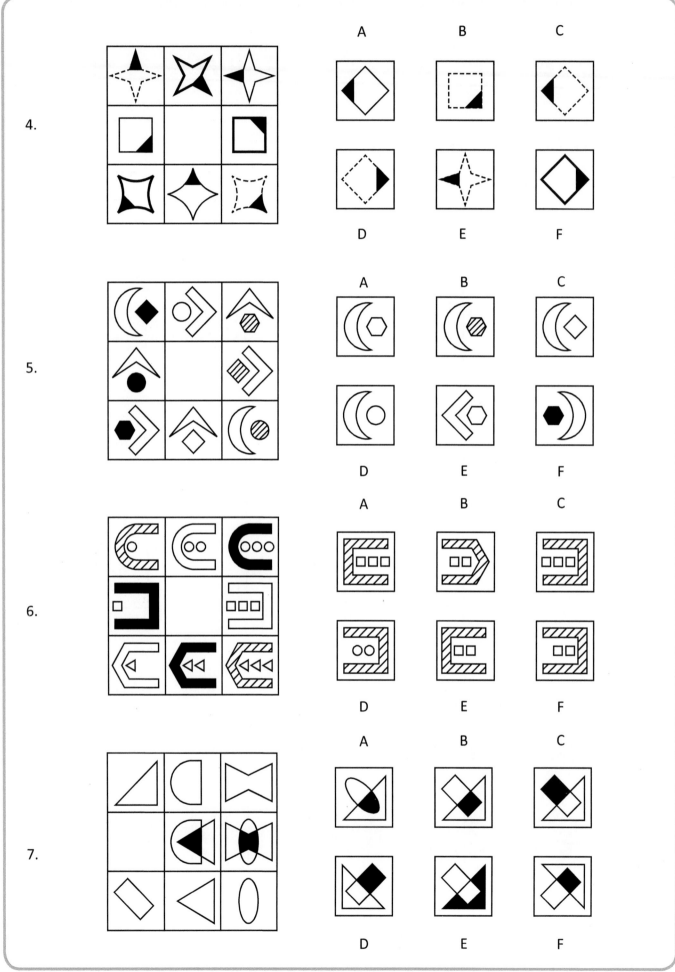

4.

A   B   C

D   E   F

5.

A   B   C

D   E   F

6.

A   B   C

D   E   F

7.

A   B   C

D   E   F

8.

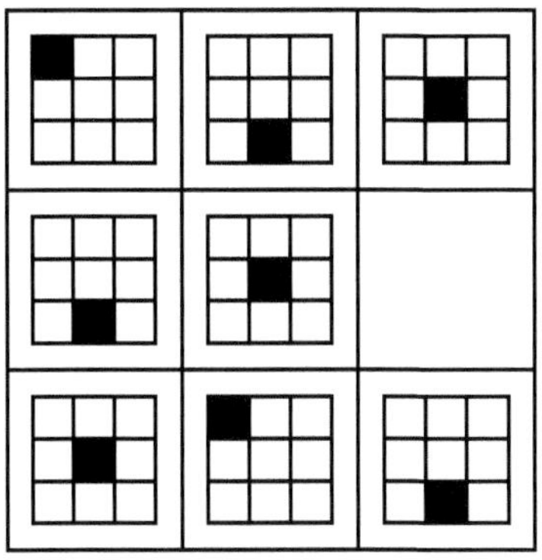

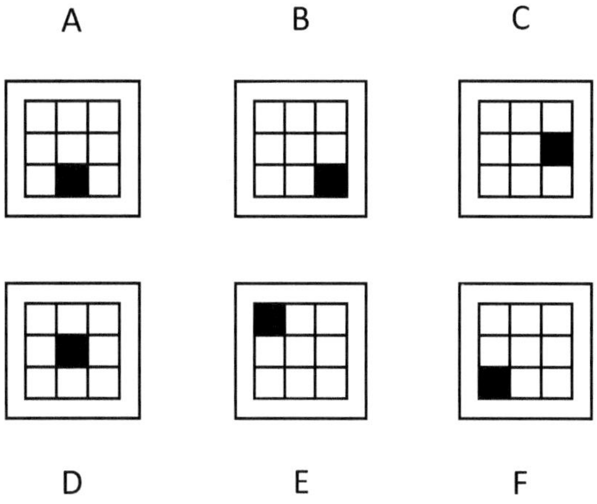

A   B   C

D   E   F

9.

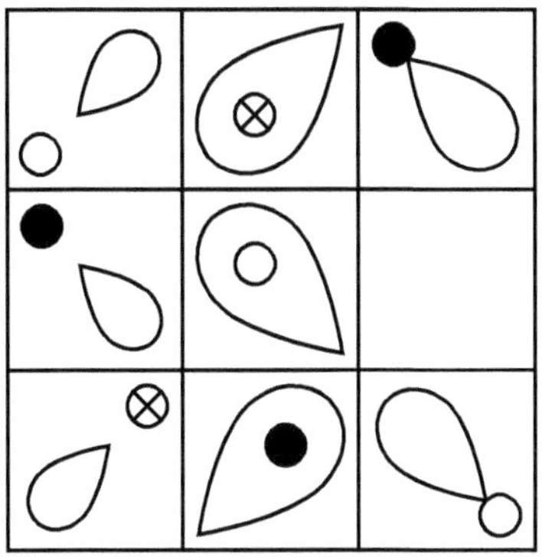

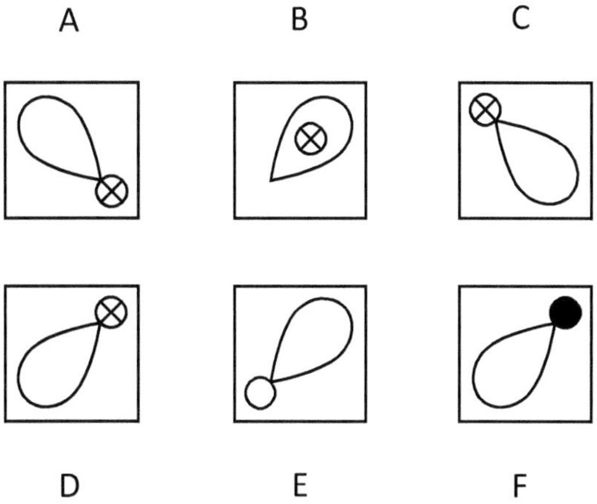

A   B   C

D   E   F

10.

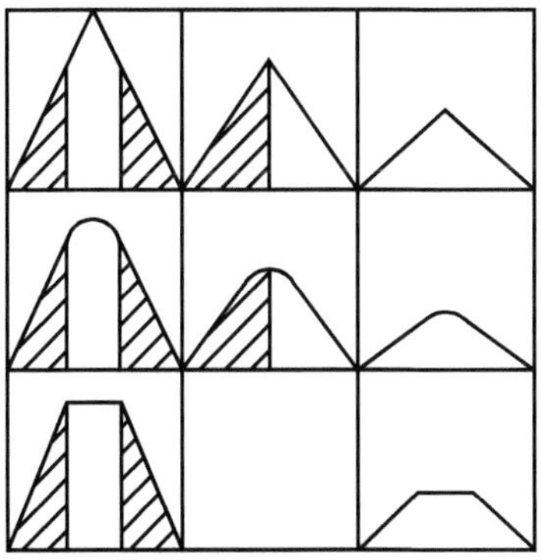

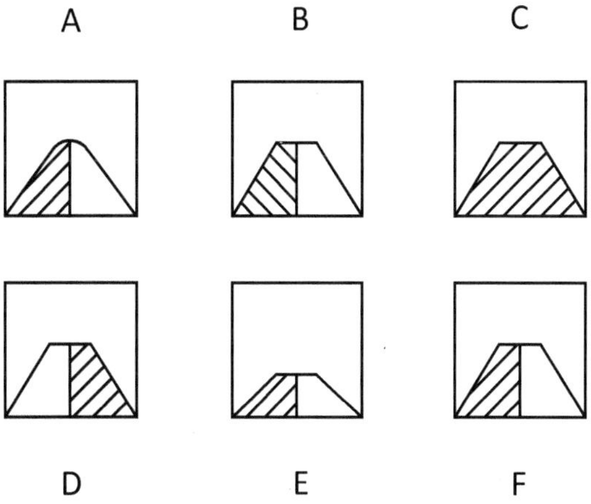

A   B   C

D   E   F

Page 31

TIMED TEST 3   **5 MINS**

Put the number 1 or 2 in the box below the correct answer and then circle the corresponding letter.

	A	B	C

1.

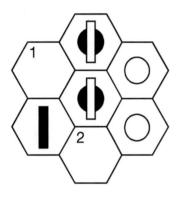

 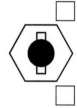

	D	E	F

	A	B	C

2.

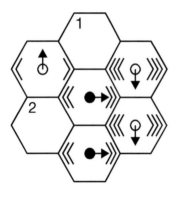

 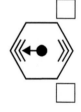

	D	E	F

	A	B	C

3.

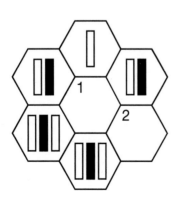

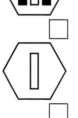

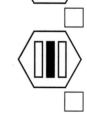

	D	E	F

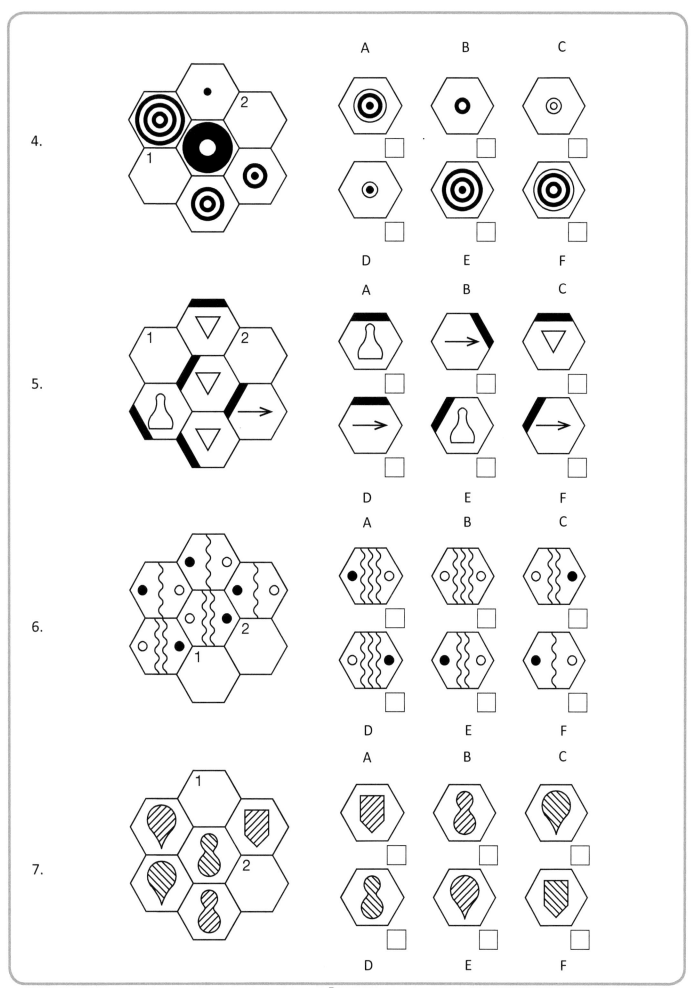

4.

A   B   C

D   E   F

5.

A   B   C

D   E   F

6.

A   B   C

D   E   F

7.

A   B   C

D   E   F

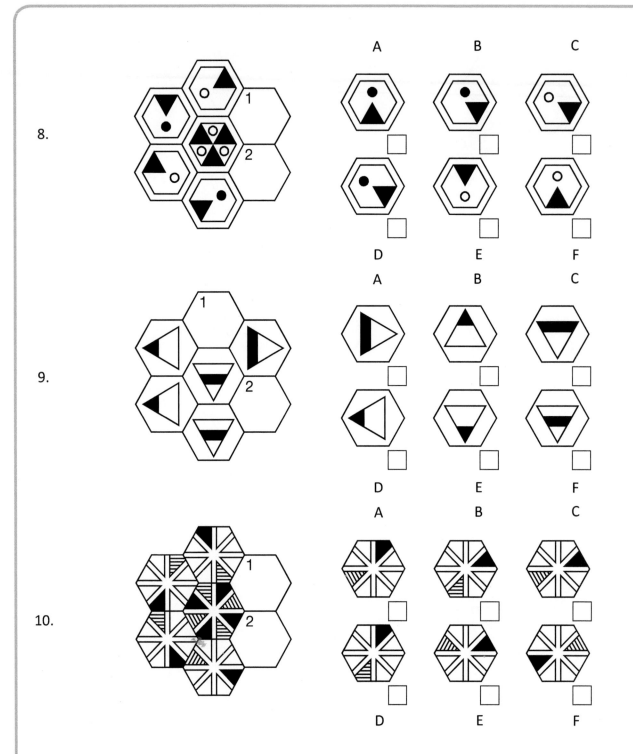

8.

9.

10.

LESSON 3:
ANALOGIES

Look out for Billy's tips and hints.

LEARN

In this question type you need to spot a relationship between two figures. Once you've discovered what has changed in the first figure to make the second figure, you can then apply the same relationship to make another pair of figures in the same way. This question type can easily be created in your home again with everyday objects as with odd one out questions in the first lesson.

An example in words might help you understand this more easily – for example, 'Kitten is to Cat as Puppy is to ....?' Here the first item is a baby animal and the second item is that baby animal grown up. The third item is another baby animal and so you have to think of what animal it might become when grown up – Dog.

Warm-up task

Think about what has changed between the first and second items, then apply this change from the third item to make the fourth item. Draw what the fourth item should be in the empty box.

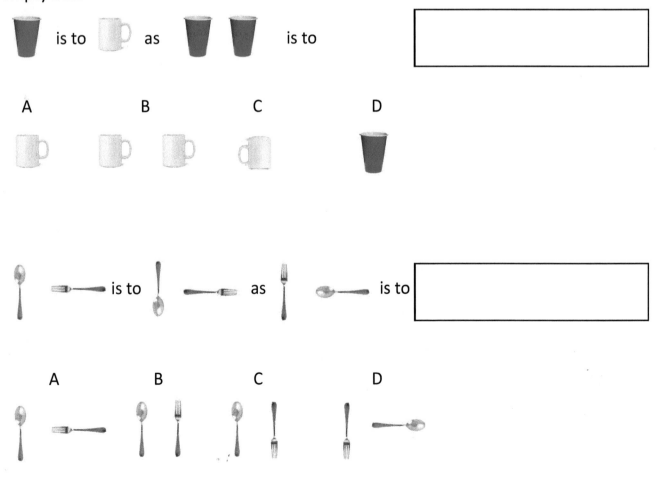

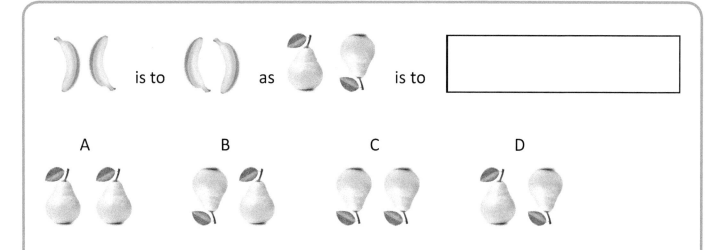

More complex analogies may have more than one change between each pair. If more than one change is taking place, use each change to rule out some answer options. Sometimes the pairs will look completely different and this is fine; all you need to do is decide what changes have been made between the figures in each pair. Take one feature at a time when the question looks difficult.

Worked Example

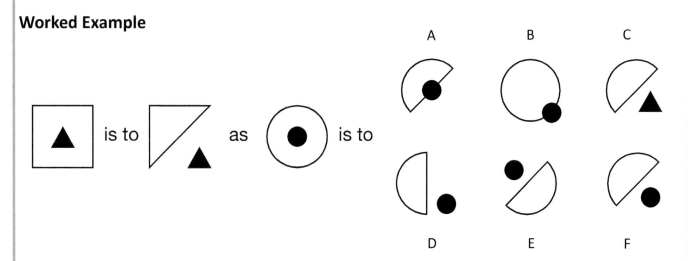

Method

(1) The first shape has a small black triangle inside a square. In the second figure the black triangle has moved to the bottom right and the square has become a right-angled triangle (or you could simply say that the square has been halved diagonally).

(2) Next, the third figure contains a small black circle inside a larger circle. Look for any answer options which don't contain the small black circle. Cross out C.

(3)   The larger circle must change to a semi-circle. So, B can be eliminated. The semi-circle must appear in the top left corner. So, options D and E can also be ruled out.

(4)   This only leaves options A and F. Only one of these shapes has the black circle in the correct position. Therefore, F is the option which completes the analogy in the best possible way.

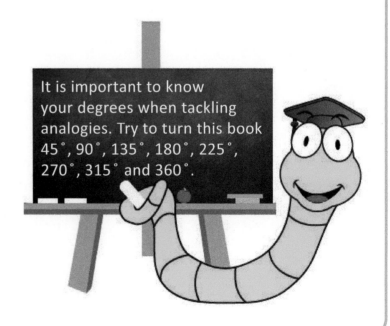

It is important to know your degrees when tackling analogies. Try to turn this book 45°, 90°, 135°, 180°, 225°, 270°, 315° and 360°.

DEVELOP

Here are some to try for yourself.

1. is to as is to

A	B	C

D	E	F

2. is to as is to

A	B	C

D	E	F

3. is to as is to

A	B	C

D	E	F

4. is to as is to

A	B	C

D	E	F

TIMED TEST 1   6 MINS

Circle the letter for each correct answer.

1. is to as is to

      A   B   C

      D   E   F

2. is to as is to

      A   B   C

      D   E   F

3. is to as is to

      A   B   C

      D   E   F

4. is to as is to

      A   B   C

      D   E   F

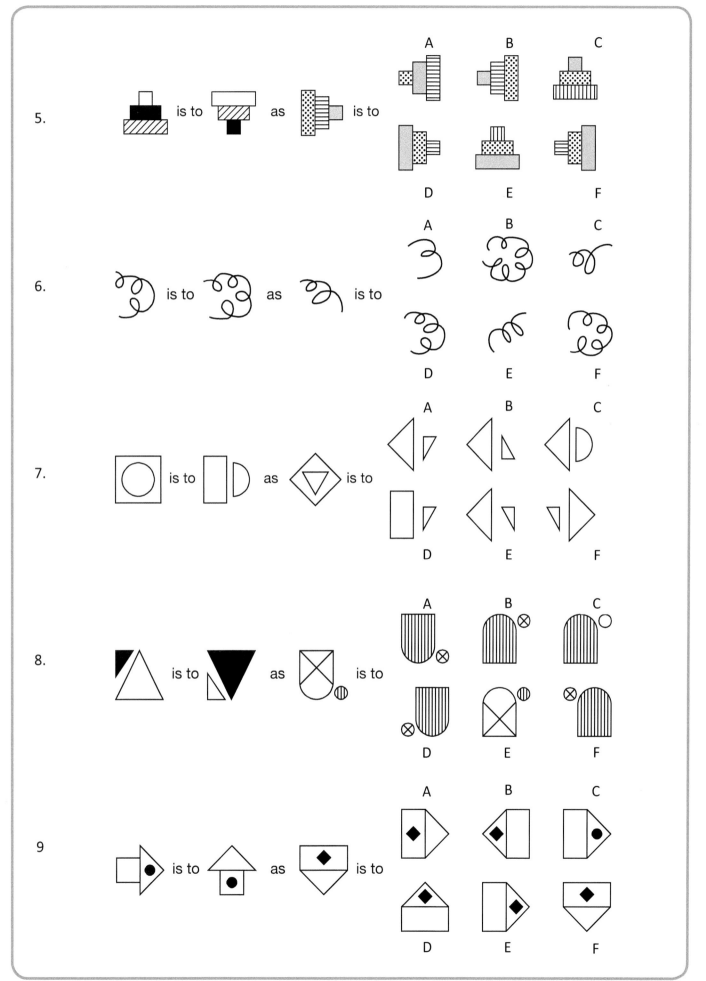

10.

11.

12.

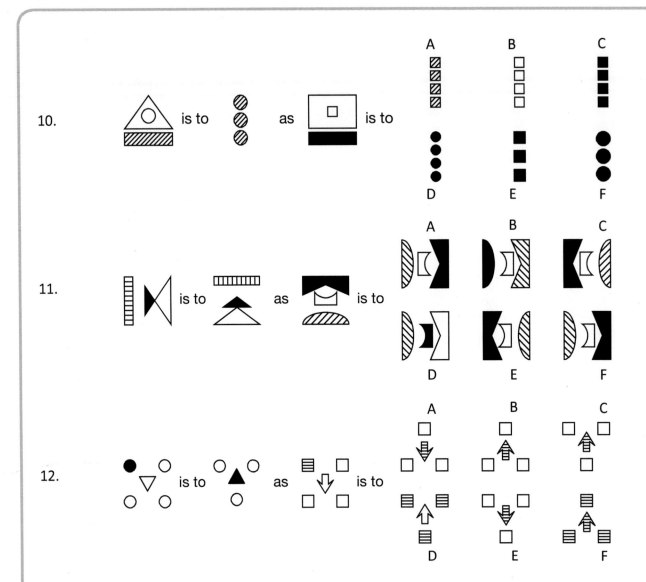

TIMED TEST 2   6 MINS

Circle the letter for each correct answer.

                A   B   C

1.  is to as  is to

                D   E   F

                A   B   C

2. is to ... as ... is to

                D   E   F

                A   B   C

3.  is to ... as ... is to

                D   E   F

                A   B   C

4. is to ... as ... is to

                D   E   F

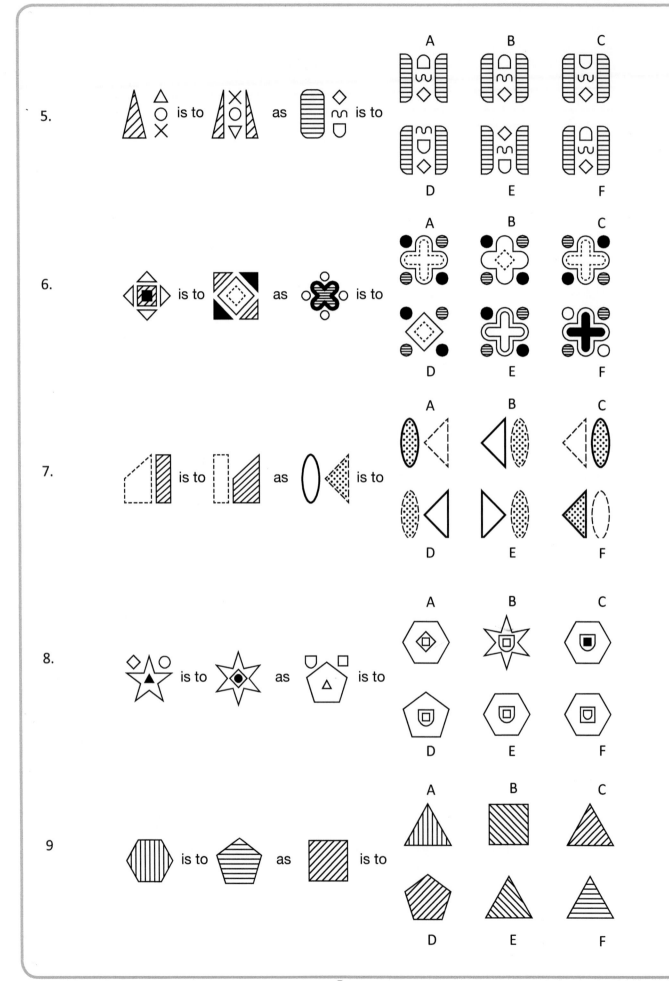

5.

6.

7.

8.

9

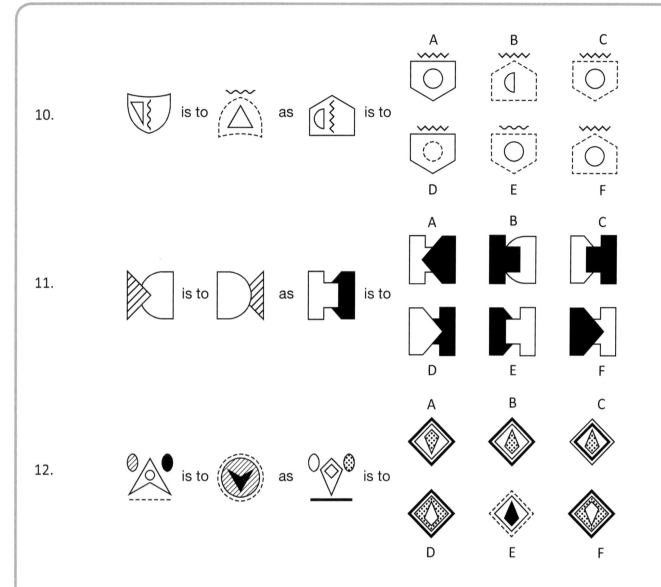

10.

11.

12.

TIMED TEST 3   **6 MINS**

Circle the letter for each correct answer.

1.

      A   B   C

      D   E   F

2.

      A   B   C

      D   E   F

3.

      A   B   C

      D   E   F

4.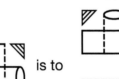

      A   B   C

      D   E   F

5.  is to  as  is to

A	B	C
D	E	F

6.  is to  as  is to

A	B	C
D	E	F

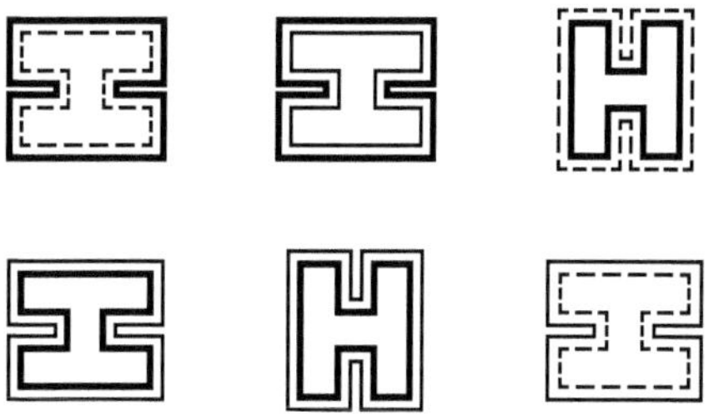

7.  is to  as 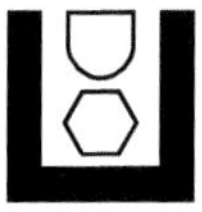 is to

A	B	C
D	E	F

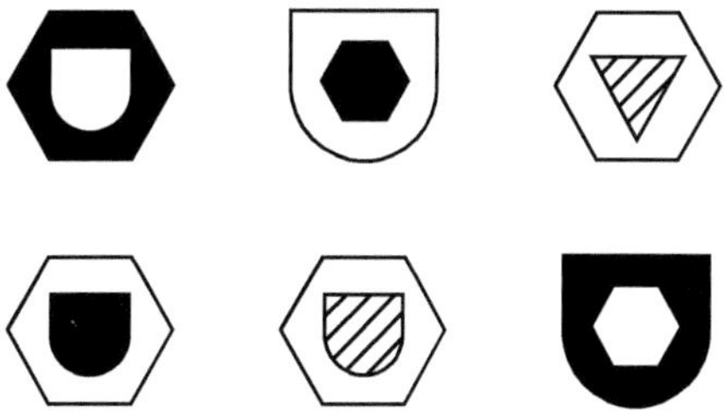

8.  is to  as  is to

A	B	C
D	E	F

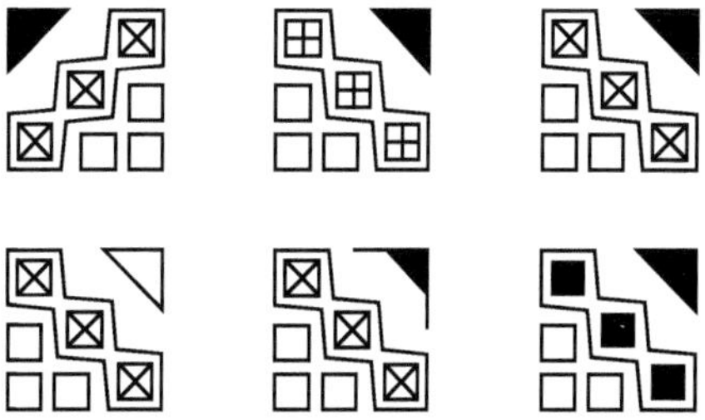

9  is to  as 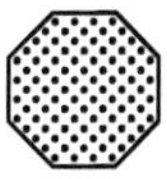 is to

A	B	C
D	E	F

10.

11.

12.

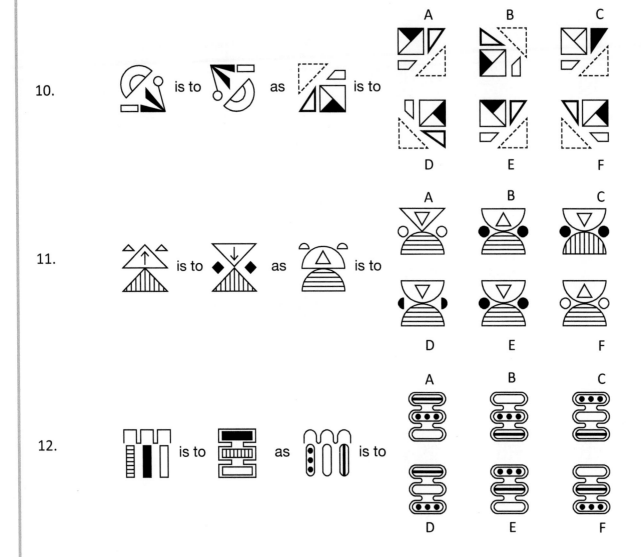

LESSON 4:
SEQUENCES

Look out for Billy's tips and hints.

LEARN

This question type involves completing a series of figures, by deciding which answer option best completes the series. You must first look carefully at how the sequence is created and then notice in which direction the series is formed. For example, if the first box is empty, then work backwards to establish the pattern. If one of the middle boxes is empty, use the figures on either side of the empty box.

Warm-up task

To help get you warmed up, here is a simple sequence which needs completing. Draw the missing figure in the empty box.

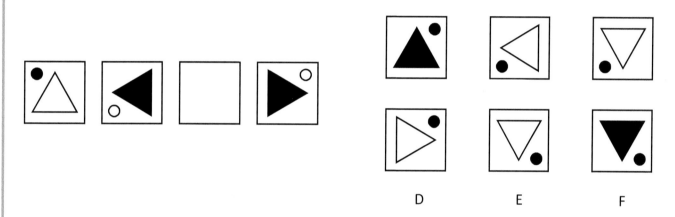

It can help to look at one feature at a time if the question is complex. Often questions will involve shapes rotating, and so it is important to know the difference between clockwise and anti-clockwise. Drawing a simple arrow can remind you in which direction the shape is moving.

Drawing the shapes that you think should go in the empty box before looking at the answer options can be useful for these questions in the same way as for the matrices questions.

(1)   First decide in which direction the series is working. As the third box is empty, look at the first two boxes and identify how the figures change. In the example above, the triangle rotates anti-clockwise 90˚. Therefore, the triangle in the empty box will need to be pointing downwards. So, eliminate answer options A, B and D.

(2)   The triangles also alternate between black and white. The triangle in the empty box will need to be white, so eliminate option F, leaving possible options C and E.

(3)   Next, look at the other feature in the pattern; the small circles. They alternate between black and white so the empty box will need to have a black circle. Options C and E both have a black circle, so now you will have to consider where they are positioned. The circles move anti-clockwise around the box. From the sequence we can see the black circle in the empty box will need to be placed in the bottom right corner. In option C the circle is on the left, so the answer must be E.

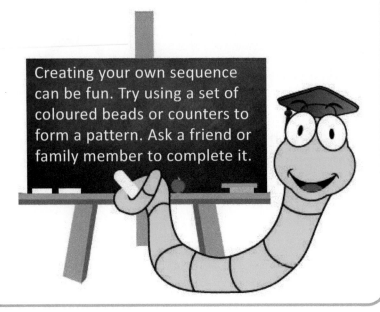

Creating your own sequence can be fun. Try using a set of coloured beads or counters to form a pattern. Ask a friend or family member to complete it.

DEVELOP

Here are some to try for yourself.

1.

A	B	C

D	E	F

2.

A	B	C

D	E	F

3.

A	B	C

D	E	F

4.

A	B	C

D	E	F

TIMED TEST 1 **6 MINS**

Circle the letter for each correct answer.

1.

    A   B   C

    D   E   F

2.

    A   B   C

    D   E   F

3.

    A   B   C

    D   E   F

4.

    A   B   C

    D   E   F

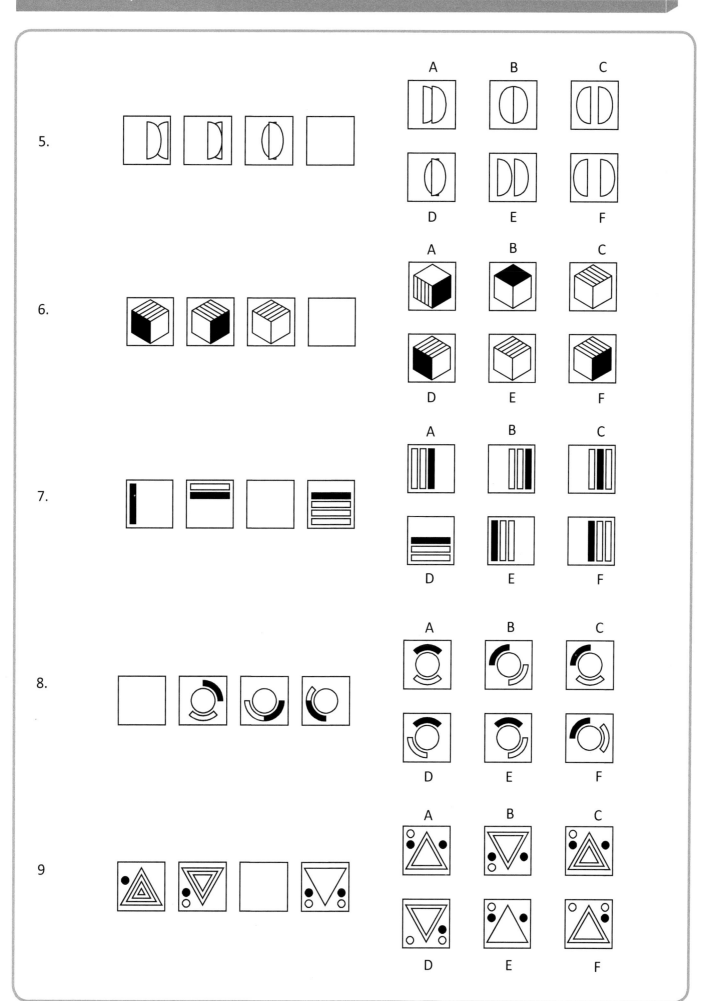

5.

6.

7.

8.

9

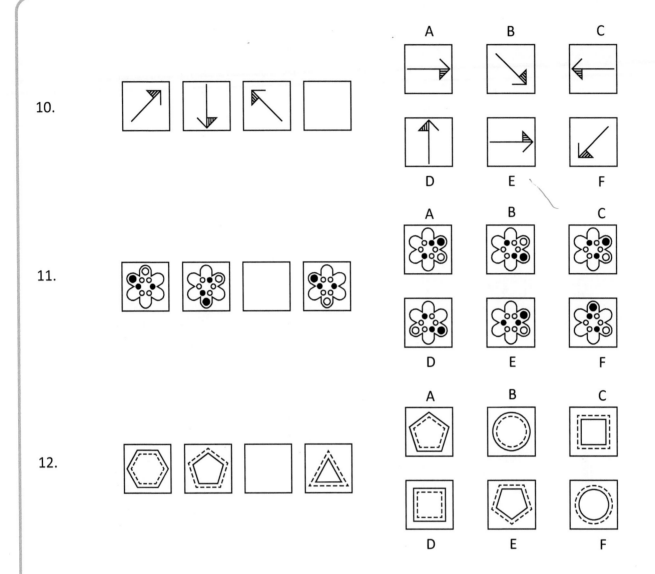

10.

11.

12.

TIMED TEST 2 **6 MINS**

Circle the letter for each correct answer.

1.

A	B	C

D	E	F

2.

A	B	C

D	E	F

3.

A	B	C

D	E	F

4.

A	B	C

D	E	F

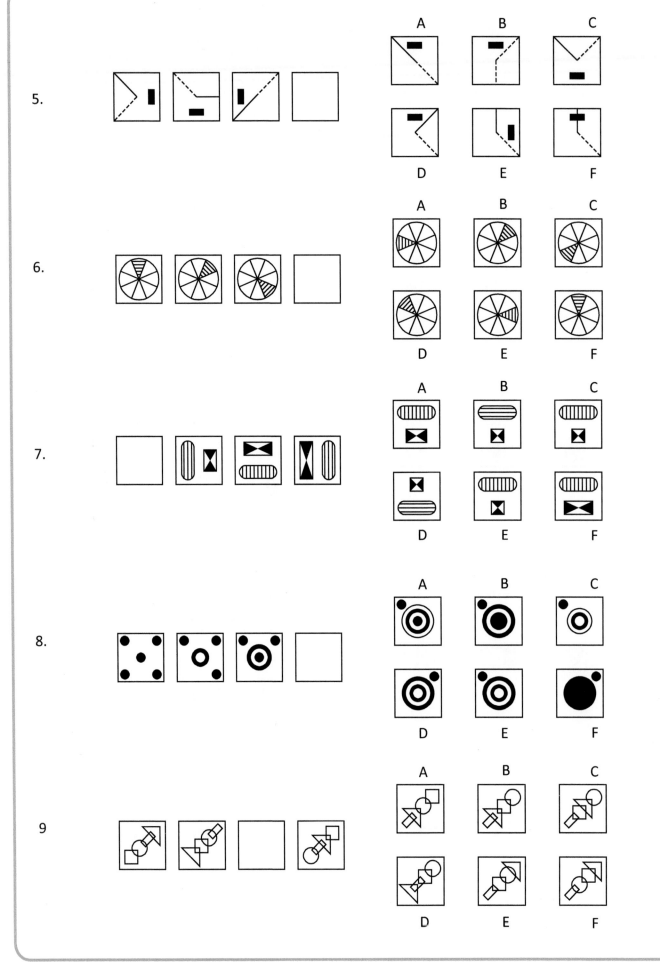

5.

6.

7.

8.

9

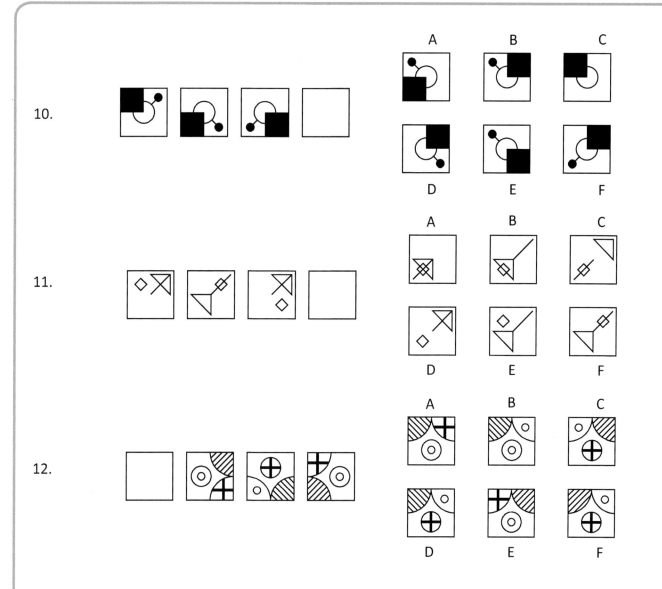

10.

11.

12.

TIMED TEST 3   6 MINS

Circle the letter for each correct answer.

1.

A   B   C

D   E   F

2.

A   B   C

D   E   F

3.

A   B   C

D   E   F

A   B   C

4.

D   E   F

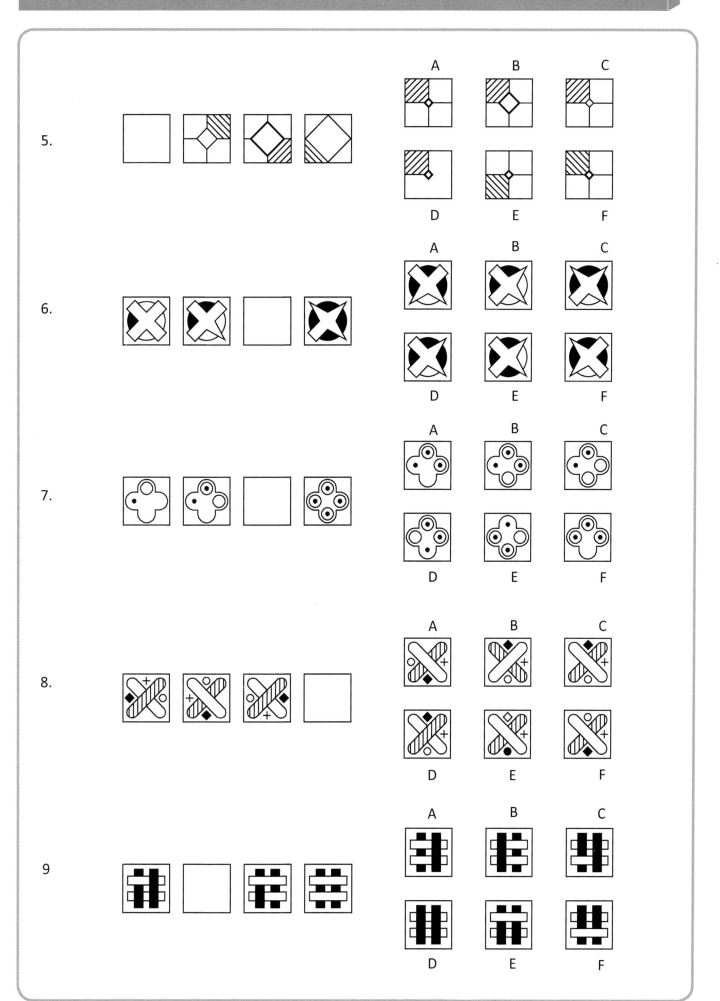

5.

6.

7.

8.

9

10.

11.

12.

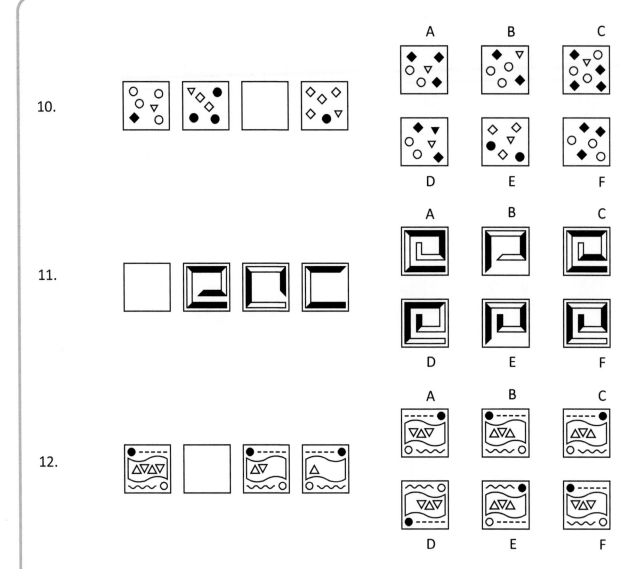

SECTION 2:
GLOSSARY AND ANSWERS

Keyword	Definition
Angle	The space between two intersecting lines.
Anti-clockwise	The opposite direction to the movement of a hands of a clock.
Clockwise	In the direction in which the hands of a clock move.
Figure	The shapes as a whole that make up one of the answer options.
Number	A quantity or amount e.g. Number of sides.
Latin square formation	Is an array filled with different symbols, each occurring exactly once in each row and exactly once in each column. | A	B	C
C	A	B
B	C	A	
Layering	When a shape is in front of or behind another shape, or where two or more shapes overlap each other.
Overlapping	To cover a shape partly by going over it's edge, to cover part of the same shape.
Position	A place where a shape is located or has been drawn e.g. top, middle or bottom of the box.
Reflection	A transformation in which a geometric figure is reflected across a line, creating a mirror image.

Rotation	The action of turning about an axis or centre.
Shading	The darkening of a shape with lines or block of colour e.g. hatched or grey.
Shape	A geometric figure such as a square, triangle or rectangle.
Size	The overall dimension or magnitude of a shape or figure.
Symmetry	When one shape becomes exactly like another if you flip, slide or turn it.

Lesson 1: Odd one out page 8

Develop page 11		
Question	Answer	Explanation
1	E	All the other figures have the same shading on the inner shape.
2	D	All the other figures have four lines.
3	D	In all the other figures the smaller overlapping circles have a black shading inside the larger circle.
4	A	All the other figures have a line of symmetry.

Timed Test 1 page 12		
Question	Answer	Explanation
1	B	In all the other figures the arrow is pointing towards the smaller square.
2	E	All the other figures have a total of nine sides.
3	B	The small black rectangles are positioned on the left of all the other figures.
4	A	The black circles are always positioned on the longest edge of the other quadrilateral.
5	C	All the black triangles point upwards in the other figures.
6	D	All the other figures contain a small, medium and large rhombus.
7	D	The white circle and black triangle must be inside the large shape.
8	E	The large shape has exactly the same smaller shape inside.
9	C	The triangle is always to the right of the circle and relative to gap between.
10	E	The other figures have the same number of circles as sides of the large shape.
11	D	All the other figures are half shaded and are not symmetrical through the vertical.
12	E	In all the other figures the arrow points upwards.
Timed Test 2 page 15		
1	D	All the other figures contain a right-angled triangle.
2	D	All the other figures have one cross on the outside of the larger shape and two crosses inside.
3	E	All the other figures have a triangle oriented towards the line.
4	A	All the other figures have a dashed line inside the bold outline.
5	E	All the other figures have a vertical line of symmetry.
6	B	All inner angles of large shape are right-angled or obtuse, B contains a reflex angle.
7	C	All are identical except for the angle of rotation. C is flipped.
8	E	The lines with a circle on the end have the circles separated by a single line.
9	D	The circle appears in a triangle where only one side belongs to the external edge of the quadrilateral shape, where as in D there are two external sides.
10	E	The small circle appears alongside the double straight line, where as in E it lies beside the curved line.
11	C	In all the other figures the square and inner triangle share the same line style.
12	D	In all the other figures the circle is positioned next to the solid band.

Timed Test 3 page 18

Question	Answer	Explanation
1	B	The double line indicates the line of symmetry, whilst the dashed line represents no line of symmetry.
2	C	The other figures contain an outer dashed line and an inner solid line.
3	C	All the figures contain 2 triangles, 1 four-sided shape and 1 other shape to complete the figure.
4	E	All the other figures have 6 sides/objects, exactly half of which are shaded.
5	C	In all the other figures when viewing the triangle in an 'upright' position the black circle is to the right of the white one.
6	A	In all the other figures the arrow head is showing a clockwise direction.
7	E	In all the other figures the left overlapping shape has a shaded part within the large shape and the right overlapping shape has a shaded part on the outside of the large shape.
8	D	All the other figures are identical except for rotation.
9	E	In all the other figures the ellipse is divided into three parts: one straight line, one jagged line and one end is shaded.
10	D	In all the other figures the black tip on the star spike is always left of the arc.
11	E	In all the other figures the two large shapes have openings in opposite directions.
12	A	In all the other figures the triangle is on the opposite side of the line from the black circle.

Lesson 2: Matrices page 22

Develop page 24

Question	Answer	Explanation
1	E	Each row contains a square, circle and triangle. These shapes all have different shading.
2	D	The black square moves clockwise 90° around the grid.
3	A	The curved line moves clockwise across the row from left to right. The dotted line is a mirror of the top row.
4	B	Each row contains a grey, hatched and black shape. The shapes increase from left to right by one more side.
5	E and D	The shapes are arranged in columns.
6	A and E	The shapes are arranged in a diagonal line from top right to base left.

Timed Test 1 page 26

Question	Answer	Explanation
1	A	The grid is a symmetrical pattern. The only difference is the black and white triangles swap shading.
2	C	The left-hand column combines with the middle column to create the right-sided column.
3	F	The pentagon rotates from left to right. The black triangle moves around the pentagon 90° clockwise.
4	F	Each row contains the same shape at the bottom, middle and top. Also, each row must have a black, grey and hatched shaded shape.

Question	Answer	Explanation
5	D	The grid pattern is diagonal, and the bottom right hatched triangle is the same shading and position in the top left corner square.
6	B	Each row contains two, three and four white circles. The black circles total four in each row.
7	B	The shapes are in latin square formation and each row is rotated 90° anti-clockwise.
8	E	The same shapes are in rows and the same shading in the columns.
9	F	Top row and middle row combine in bottom row and swap shades. Top row shape overlays shape from middle row.
10	A	Large shapes in rows and small corner shapes in columns.

Timed Test 2 page 29

Question	Answer	Explanation
1	C	The small circles and squares are in a latin square formation and the ruled shapes are in opposite latin square formation.
2	B	The small shapes are in latin square formation with the arrows in opposite latin square formation.
3	D	Whatever shapes are not shaded in the top 2 rows become shaded in the bottom row.
4	C	The shapes rotate 135° across the rows and the line styles are in latin square formation.
5	A	The large shapes are in latin square formation and the small shapes are in opposite latin square formation. The shading of the small shapes are in columns.
6	F	The large shapes are in rows and the same number of the small shapes are in columns. The shading of large shapes are in latin square formation.
7	B	The top and bottom rows combine in the middle row and where they overlap they are shaded.
8	E	The shapes are in latin square formation.
9	D	The teardrop shapes rotate 90° clockwise going down the columns. The small circles are in latin square formation.
10	F	The height and division of shapes are in columns. Each shape has the same top in each row.

Timed Test 3 page 32

Question	Answer	Explanation
1	C and D	The shapes are arranged in columns.
2	A and E	The shapes are arranged in columns.
3	B and F	The shapes are arranged across rows that dip in the centre column.
4	E and B	The circles increase by one in a clockwise direction with alternating shades of circles. The largest circle is always black.
5	E and D	The central shapes are in columns. The black edges are in a diagonal formation from top left to base right.
6	A and C	The shapes are arranged across rows that rise in the centre column.
7	B and F	The shapes are in columns and the shading in rows that rise in the centre column.

8	D and F	The triangles and circles in the hexagons rotate 60° clockwise and the circles alternate shade.
9	F and A	The shapes are in columns and the bold shading remains the same.
10	D and C	The shaded segments both move one segment clockwise in a clockwise direction around the matrix from the top of the hexagon.

Lesson 3: Analogies page 36

Develop page 39

Question	Answer	Explanation
1	E	The left-hand box changes to the right-hand side and the vertical lines switch to horizontal lines.
2	B	The shapes move one box at a time in a clockwise direction.
3	C	The figure increases by one more side and an additional dashed line is added to the inside.
4	D	All the shapes are a mirror image of the opposite side.

Timed Test 1 page 40

Question	Answer	Explanation
1	A	The right-sided hatched shaded column moves to become the left column and the whole figure rotates 90° clockwise.
2	E	The arrow moves 90° anti-clockwise. The black square moves clockwise.
3	B	The whole figure rotates 90° and the shading changes between the shapes.
4	A	The figures gain one more additional line and there is always a line from the top left of the square to the centre.
5	F	The shape rotates 180°. The shading of the top square moves to the bottom rectangle, the middle-hatched rectangle moves to the smaller square and the dotted rectangle moves to the middle-sized rectangle.
6	D	One additional loop is created from one figure to the next.
7	A	The shapes halve vertically and the large one moves to the left and the smaller to the right.
8	B	The shapes reflect on horizontally and swap shading.
9	E	The shape rotates 90° anti-clockwise and the small inner shape of the larger one then takes shading from the lower rectangle
10	C	The small inner shape multiplies to the number of sides of the larger shape and then takes the shading from the lower rectangle.
11	F	The figure rotates 90° clockwise and the central smaller shape flips sides.
12	C	The figure flips and the centre shape takes the shade of the outer corner shape which disappears. The remaining small shape on that side centralises.

Timed Test 2 page 43		
Question	Answer	Explanation
1	E	The cross lines become dashed and the base shape moves to the top. The other two shapes reflect on a 45° line and swap shades.
2	A	Shapes flip on a vertical line and the outer lines swap places. The small shapes centralise and the lower shape enlarges and moves behind the other shape.
3	B	The top shape moves to the bottom moving the other two shapes up. The line style moves to the top moving the other line styles down.
4	E	The shape rotates 90° anti-clockwise. The base shape then flips and its content flips to the inside top of the other shape.
5	F	The shape on the left splits vertically and sandwiches inverted small shapes.
6	A	The shape rotates 45° and enlarges. Centre shade goes to top right and base left triangle. Larger centre shape shade goes to top left and base right triangle. Centre small shape outline becomes dashed.
7	B	The shapes swap places and take each other's attributes.
8	E	There is an additional point/side to the large shape. The top left shape contains a smaller version of the top right shape in the centre of the large shape. The small shape takes the shading from the previous central shape.
9	E	The figures reduce by one side and striped shading rotates 90°.
10	C	The large shape flips and the solid line becomes a dashed line. The entire inside line rotates 90° and moves above the shape. The other inner shape doubles size by flipping across.
11	F	The shapes flip vertically and swap places in front of/behind each other.
12	B	The small inner shape enlarges and becomes double-lined; new outer line style taken from base line, fill taken from upper left ellipse. Large shape flips, shrinks and takes shade from upper right ellipse.

Timed Test 3 page 46		
Question	Answer	Explanation
1	C	The four small shapes stay in position and the larger two shapes rotate 90° and the lines becomes dashed.
2	E	The shapes rotates 135° anti-clockwise and the shading moves to the other part of the shape.
3	D	The shape rotates 90° clockwise and the line style of the main part of the shape swaps.
4	D	The main shape shrinks and swaps shade with upper left small shape which enlarges, rotates 90° and contains small upper right shape which also rotates 90°.
5	F	The shape rotates 90° and the central bar takes shade from the left half of the shape. The shapes on the side merge behind the bar and swap line style.
6	D	The shapes rotate 90° and swap line style.
7	B	The small upper inner shape enlarges. The lower inner shape enlarges and centres in the new upper shape taking the shading from the large outer shape.
8	C	The shapes flip on vertical and the smaller shapes swap fill.

9	A	The shape divides into four. Top right and lower left quadrants lose fill and have thicker outlines.
10	E	The shapes rotate 180°.
11	E	The upper half of the figure flips. The small shapes double in size and become a solid fill.
12	B	The figure rotates 90° clockwise and the line duplicates to the left and surrounds inner bars. The two uppermost bars swap shade.

Lesson 4: Sequences page 51

Develop page 53

Question	Answer	Explanation
1	F	The black circle moves clockwise around the square. The square increases in size and rotates 90°.
2	C	A repeating alternate pattern. The figure will be the same as in the second square.
3	B	The shapes increase by one more side moving from left to right.
4	A	A repeating pattern and working from right to left, the figure in the first square will be the same as in the third square.

Timed Test 1 page 54

Question	Answer	Explanation
1	E	The figure rotates 90° clockwise.
2	D	The figure moves 90° anti-clockwise and the black shading changes through the three shapes.
3	F	The number of dots increases by one more from left to right. The dots move clockwise 45° around the square.
4	A	The dotted line moves 45° anti-clockwise. The bold line moves clockwise 45°.
5	B	The semi-circle behind moves gradually right to left across the box until it appears.
6	C	The cube rotates 90° clockwise from left to right
7	F	The bar rotates 90° clockwise. Additional bar is added and is always white, pushing the solid bar further into the cell.
8	B	The black arc rotates 90° clockwise around the circle. The white arc rotates 45° clockwise around the circle.
9	A	Triangle flips and loses smallest triangle each time. Additional circle is added – black then white above, swap sides and repeat.
10	E	The arrow rotates 135° clockwise.
11	C	The large white circle moves one 'petal' clockwise. The large black circle moves two 'petals' anti-clockwise and the small circles rotate as a group 60° anti-clockwise.
12	D	One fewer sides to shape and outlines alternate between solid and dashed.

Timed Test 2 page 57

| 1 | C | The square moves from the top left corner to bottom right corner and the shaded segment of the square rotates 90°. The opposing diagonal bar is in the centre two cells. |
| 2 | B | The shapes rotate 90° anti-clockwise. Large triangle divides into 2, 3 and then 4 parts alternating shade. |

3	E	The circle emerges a quarter at a time anti-clockwise. Each time the far left half remains shaded.
4	D	The figure rotates 90° clockwise and gains a solid rectangle each time. The circle alternates shade.
5	F	The black rectangle rotates 90° clockwise and the dashed line rotates 90° anti-clockwise. The solid line rotates 135° clockwise.
6	A	The striped segment rotates 1 space clockwise then skips one space then skips 2 places.
7	C	All rotates 90° anti-clockwise and the shade of the lozenge shape is always vertical stripe. The rectangle stretches in each cell.
8	E	One fewer circles in corners anti-clockwise. One additional circle in centre alternating shade.
9	B	The top right shape moves to base left and the other shapes move up.
10	B	The black circle on the short line rotates 90° clockwise. The corner square rotates 90° anti-clockwise around the cell.
11	B	The triangle alternates between the top right and base left corners and the small square rotates 90° clockwise.
12	D	All rotates 90° clockwise and the centre circle and left quarter circle swap shades.

Timed Test 3 page 60

Question	Answer	Explanation
1	F	The image flips on a vertical and there is one less 'arm' per cell. The line styles alternates between thin and thick.
2	E	Additional triangle per cell moving existing triangle anti-clockwise.
3	C	The dashed line alternates position between the left side and base of the cell. The arrow rotates, anchored on the top right anti-clockwise 30°. The solid circle moves from top right to base left.
4	F	The large shape pattern alternates and there is an additional black circle per cell.
5	A	The central square enlarges and the line style alternates between thick and thin. The striped quadrant rotates 90° clockwise.
6	D	Additional quarter circle shaded clockwise. The square end of the cross becomes pointed in anti-clockwise direction.
7	B	An additional small black circle and an open circle is added each time 90° clockwise around the shape.
8	C	The striped bar alternates between being in front of and behind the white bar. Small shapes rotate 90° anti-clockwise.
9	E	The white bars come to the front section one at a time in a clockwise direction.
10	A	There is always 1 triangle, 1 additional square and 1 fewer circles. The circles and squares swap shade.
11	F	There is one fewer lengths of figure from the centre. Bar nearest the centre always shaded and the rest alternates shade.
12	C	The shapes all flip on a vertical except for the triangles. There is also one fewer triangles per cell from the right.

Fill in the tables below with your results from each of the Timed Tests.

Colour the Progress Grid on the next page to see how well you have done.

Odd one out

Section 1	Timed Test 1	Timed Test 2	Timed Test 3
Score	/12	/12	/12

Matrices

Section 2	Timed Test 1	Timed Test 3	Timed Test 3
Score	/10	/10	/10

Analogies

Section 3	Timed Test 1	Timed Test 2	Timed Test 3
Score	/12	/12	/12

Sequences

Section 4	Timed Test 1	Timed Test 2	Timed Test 3
Score	/12	/12	/12

Colour the grids below with your total mark from each Timed Test to see how well you have done.

Odd one out

Timed Test 1

Timed Test 2

Timed Test 3

Matrices

Timed Test 1

Timed Test 2

Timed Test 3

Analogies

Timed Test 1

Timed Test 2

Timed Test 3

Sequences

Timed Test 1

Timed Test 2

Timed Test 3

Read the statements below for some hints and tips.

0–5: Carefully re-read the 'Learn' section and try the 'Develop' questions again. When you feel confident, retry the Timed Test.

6–8: Good effort, make sure you learn from your mistakes. Review the answers of the questions that you have got wrong and try to understand the techniques required.

9+: Well done, you have shown a secure understanding.